Winnie

Lii

Wisdom

Inspired by A.A.Milne & illustrated by E.H.Shepard

EGMONT

We bring stories to life

Published in Great Britain 2013
by Egmont UK Limited
The Yellow Building, Nicholas Road, London W11 4AN
© 2013 Disney Enterprises, Inc
Based on the Winnie-the-Pooh works by A.A.Milne & E.H.Shepard

ISBN 978 1 4052 6704 5

"It isn't Brain," said Pooh humbly, "because You Know Why; but it comes to me sometimes."

Before you Begin

Pooh is a Bear of Very Little Brain who can't always think of the right words to say, but even so has said some very wise words and thought some very interesting thoughts, which he would like to share with you. Poetry and Hums and little Words of Wisdom aren't things which Pooh gets, they are things which get *him*. All he can do is go where they can find him. So, reader go where they can find *you*, too and dip your paws into this little collection of Wisdom from an Astute and Helpful Bear, The Best Bear in All the World, Winnie-the-Pooh.

Personal Thoughts

When you are a Bear of very Little Brain, and you Think of Things, you sometimes find that a Thing which seemed very Thingish inside you is quite different when it gets out in the open and has other people looking at it.

Set Priorities

Nearly eleven o' clock is time for
a little smackerel of something.

Check your Store Cupboard

It's sort of comforting to know if you
have fourteen pots of honey left, or fifteen,
as the case may be.

Anticipation

Although Eating Honey is a very good thing
to do, there is a moment just before you begin
to eat it which is better than when you are.

Plan Ahead

Many a bear going out on a warm day would never think of bringing a little something with him.

Have a Friendly Day

When you've been walking in the wind for miles, and you suddenly go into somebody's house, and he says, "Hallo, Pooh, you're just in time for a little smackerel of something," and you are, then it's what I call a Friendly Day.

Take Time to Relax

What I like *doing* best is Nothing. It's when
people call out at you just as you're going off to
do it, "What are you going to do?" and you say
"Oh Nothing," and then you go and do it.
Doing Nothing means just going along,
listening to all the things you can't hear,
and not bothering.

Control your Stress Levels

To seem quite at ease hum tiddely-pom once or twice in a what-shall-we-do-now kind of way.

A Little Caution

When you go after honey with a
balloon, the great thing is not to let the
bees know you're coming.

A Matter of Taste

The wrong sort of bees would
make the wrong sort of honey.

Cold Hard Logic

It's no good going home to practise
a Special Outdoor Song which Has To
Be Sung In The Snow.

Keep Busy

It's just the day for doing things.

Don't Procrastinate

If you're always saying,
"We'll see,"
nothing ever happens.

Assess your Surroundings

When your house doesn't look like a house
and looks like a tree that has been blown down,
it is time you tried to find another one.

Supposition

Supposing a tree fell down when
you were underneath it?

Supposing it didn't.

Expediency

You never know when a bit of
string might be Useful.

Insight

It's best to know what you are
looking for before you look for it.

Accept Yourself

"Pooh," said Rabbit kindly,
   "you haven't any brain."
"I know," said Pooh humbly.

Improve your Brain Power

How wonderful to have a Real Brain
which could tell you things.

Understanding

Rabbit is clever. Rabbit has Brain.
I suppose that's why he never
understands anything.

Self Knowledge

Pooh hasn't much Brain, but he never comes to any harm. He does silly things and they turn out right.

You Can't be Good at Everything

When you are a Bear of Very Little Brain
you're never much good at riddles.

Management Skills

A Very Clever Brain could catch a Heffalump
if he knew the right way to go about it.

Knowledge

If you stood on the bottom rail of a bridge, and leant over, and watched the river slipping slowly away beneath you, you would suddenly know everything that there is to be known.

Keeping Trim

A bear, however hard he tries,
Grows tubby without exercise.

Why You Can't

It all comes of *liking* honey so much.

Companionship

It isn't much good having anything exciting,
if you can't share it with somebody.

It's so much more friendly with two.

Admire Someone

You can't help respecting anybody who can spell

TUESDAY.

Self Appreciation

"What sort of stories does he like?"
"About himself. Because he's *that* sort of Bear."

The Best Bear in all the World.

Time Management

"They always take longer than you think."
said Rabbit.
"How long do you *think* they'll take?"
asked Roo.

Action

When you have nothing else
to do, do something.

Decision making

When you've been thinking you can
come to some very important decisions.

Take the Initiative

Like Rabbit, never let things come
to you, always go out and fetch them.

Organisation

Is what happens when you
do a search and you don't all look
in the same place at once.

Be Prepared

Brush the honey off your nose, spruce yourself
up so as to look Ready for Anything.

Sociability

A good reason for going to see
everybody is because it's Thursday.

A Little Philosophy

Sometimes, the more you think,
the more there *is* no real answer.

Whenever you Feel Afraid

To show you haven't been frightened
jump up and down once or twice in an
exercising sort of way.

Make a Brave Gesture

Just hum to yourself as if you are
waiting for something.

Anxious Moments

If you look round and see a Very Fierce
Heffalump looking down at you, sometimes
you forget what you were going to say.

Be Careful!

You can never tell with bees, you can never tell
with paw-marks, and you can *never* tell
with Heffalumps.

Don't Worry

When you get a sinking feeling,
don't worry, it's probably because
you're hungry.

Practise the Art of Disguise

When asked if that's you, pretend
it isn't you and see what happens.

Spare Time

While you wonder what to do,
sit down and sing a song.

Punctuality

Don't be late for whatever you want to
be in time for.

Try a Little Spontaneity

Do a Good thing to Do without
thinking about it.

If at First you Don't Succeed

If the string breaks,
try another piece of string.

Find Comfort

Nobody can be un-cheered with a balloon.

Say it With Flowers

How sad it is to be animal who has never
had a bunch of Violets picked for him.

Gastronomic Disappointment

A Very Nearly tea is one you
forget about afterwards.

Confusion

Pooh looked at his two paws. He knew that
one of them was the right, and he knew that
when you had decided which one of them was
the right, then the other one was the left, but
he could never remember how to begin.

Solving Storage Problems

A Useful Pot can make you glad.
It's for putting things in.

Always Ask

Being a Faithful Knight might mean you just go
on being faithful without being told things.

Look on the Bright Side

Everybody is all right *really*.
That's what *I* think.

Manners

Always say Goodbye-and-
thank-you-for-a-nice-time.

Be Open to Creativity

Poetry and Hums aren't things which you get, they're things which get *you*. All you can do is to go where they can find you.

Bravery

To only blinch inside is the bravest way for
A Very Small Animal not to blinch that there is.

Make Yourself Needed

Without Pooh the adventure would be
impossible. . . Impossible without Me!
That sort of Bear.

Love your Neighbour as Yourself

"Oh Bear!" said Christopher Robin.
"How I do love you!"
"So do I," said Pooh.

Enjoy Yourself

What I like best in the whole world is
Me and Piglet going to see You, and You saying
"What about a little something?" and Me saying,
"Well, I shouldn't mind a little something,
should you, Piglet," and it being a hummy sort
of day outside, and birds singing.

Learn from Experience

"That's funny," said Pooh. "I dropped it
on the other side," said Pooh, "and it came out
on this side! I wonder if it would do it again?"
And he went back for some more fir-cones.
It did. It kept on doing it.

Look Out!

An Ambush is a sort of surprise.
So is a gorse-bush sometimes.

Listening Skills

There are twelve pots of honey in my cupboard and they've been calling me for hours. I couldn't hear them properly before because Rabbit would keep talking, but if nobody says anything except those twelve pots, then I shall know where they're coming from.

Be Caring

A little Consideration, a little Thought
for Others, makes all the difference.

Also available:

Eeyore's
Little Book of
Gloom

Read this book – then you'll be sorry . . .

ISBN 978 I 4052 6705 2

Tigger's
Little Book of
Bounce

Tiggers can do anything – and so can you!

ISBN 978 1 4052 6706 9